PUBLIC SCHOOL 242
FLATLANDS AVE. & EAST 100 ST.
BROOKLYN, 12, N. Y.

THE MACMILLAN READERS

Today We Go

ARTHUR I. GATES
MIRIAM BLANTON HUBER
FRANK SEELY SALISBURY

THE MACMILLAN COMPANY : NEW YORK

Illustrated by
CHARLES PAYZANT AND ASSOCIATES
HELEN HANSEN, SYLVIA HOLLAND, JANET PAGE, BASIL DAVIDOVICH, ERNEST TERRAZAS

© *The Macmillan Company* 1951, 1957

All Rights Reserved

PRINTED IN THE UNITED STATES OF AMERICA

ACKNOWLEDGMENTS

Grateful acknowledgment is made to the following authors and publishers for permission to use copyrighted material:

Gertrude Blumenthal, for "Louise and the Subway," adapted by permission, from *Louise's Adventure: Her Ride in the Subway*, by Gertrude Blumenthal; copyright, 1941 by Gertrude Blumenthal.

Dodd, Mead & Company, Inc., for "There Was Tammie!" adapted by permission of Dodd, Mead & Company, from *There Was Tammie!* by Dorothy and Marguerite M. Bryan; copyright, 1935, by Dorothy M. Bryan.

The Fideler Company, for "Where Is Christopher?" adapted by permission, from *Where Is Christopher?* by Anne Lawrence; copyright, 1946, by The Fideler Company.

Harcourt, Brace and Company, Inc., for "The Burro That Had a Name," adapted by permission, from *The Burro That Had a Name*, by Lorraine and Jerrold Beim; copyright, 1939, by Harcourt, Brace and Company, Inc.

Charlotte Huber, for "Bobby Rides a Bus," written for this book; all rights reserved.

Joseph Joel Keith, for "Young Horse Running," written for this book; all rights reserved.

ACKNOWLEDGMENTS *(cont.)*

The Macmillan Company, for "Good Pony, Blaze!" adapted by permission, from *Billy and Blaze*, by C. W. Anderson, copyright, 1936, by The Macmillan Company; for "Blaze and the Forest Fire," adapted by permission, from *Blaze and the Forest Fire*, by C. W. Anderson, copyright, 1938, by The Macmillan Company; for "Skyscrapers," by Rachel Field, reprinted by permission, from *The Pointed People*, by Rachel Field, copyright, 1930, by The Macmillan Company.

The Marcel Rodd Company, for "Smoky and the Red Fire Engine," adapted by permission, from *Smokey and the Red Fire Engine*, by Joe DeMers; copyright, 1945, by Joseph DeMers.

The Viking Press, Inc., for "Indian Boy's Song," by Ann Nolan Clark, reprinted by permission of The Viking Press, Inc., New York, from *In My Mother's House*, by Ann Nolan Clark; copyright, 1941, by Ann Nolan Clark.

Albert Whitman & Company, for "Now We Fly," adapted by permission, from *Today We Fly*, by Margaret Friskey; copyright, 1942, by Albert Whitman & Company.

Stories

Dick and Nancy 7
  Our Postman 8
  Our Friends 16
  A New Home Far Away . . . 20
  From Bob and Susan 24
  Our Big Book 29

Other Boys and Girls 39
  Where Is Christopher?
    Anne Lawrence 41
  The Burro That Had a Name
    Lorraine and *Jerrold Beim* 56
  Indian Boy's Song (Verse)
    Ann Nolan Clark 70

Billy and Blaze 71
  Good Pony, Blaze!
    C. W. Anderson 73
  Blaze and the Forest Fire
    C. W. Anderson 86
  Young Horse Running (Verse)
    Joseph Joel Keith 98

Tammie and Smoky 99
  There Was Tammie!
    Dorothy and *Marguerite Bryan* 101
  Smoky and the Red Fire Engine
    Joseph DeMers 115

Today We Ride 127
  Bobby Rides a Bus
    Charlotte Huber 129
  Louise and the Subway
    Gertrude Blumenthal 143
  Skyscrapers (Verse)
    Rachel Field 157
  Now We Fly
    Margaret Friskey 158

Dick and Nancy

Our Postman

"Dick and Nancy!" called Mother.
"Has the postman come?"

"No, Mother," said Nancy.
"But it is time for him to come."

"The postman is on his way now," said Dick.
"I saw the dogs go running."

Mother laughed.
"Then he is coming," she said.

Down the street
came the postman.
 The dogs were with him.
 Little dogs, big dogs!
 All the dogs on the street
came with the postman.

 Every day the dogs
looked for the postman.
 He was the friend
of all the dogs on the street.
 When they saw him coming,
they went running to him.

"Here he is," said Dick.
"Here is our postman
with his friends, the dogs."

"How do you do, Mr. Postman?"
said Nancy.
"Have you something for us?"

"Yes, Nancy," said the postman.
"Here is a letter for your mother.
Here are some letters
for your father, too."

"Oh, Mr. Postman!" said Nancy.
"Don't you have something for me?"

"Let me see," said the postman.
"Yes, Nancy, I do have something for you.
Here is a pretty card with your name on it."

"Thank you," said Nancy.
"I was looking for that card.
I am so happy to get it."

The postman gave the letters to Dick.
"Take them to your mother," he said.

"Dick," said Nancy.
"When you come back,
I want you to see my card."

Dick ran into the house.
"Mother, here are your letters,"
he called.

"Thank you, Dick," said Mother.

Down the street went the postman.
With him went the dogs.

The dogs ran and played.
They were happy to be
with the postman.
He was a friend.

Into the houses went the postman.
He had many letters and cards
for the mothers and fathers,
and for the boys and girls, too.

When the postman went into a house,
the dogs stopped on the street.
When the postman came out,
the dogs went on with him.

The postman came to the end of the street.

"Now, dogs," he said.

"This is the end of your street. You must go home now.

But I have something for you before you go."

The postman did have something for the dogs.

He had something for every one of them.

Many of the mothers on the street
gave the postman things for the dogs.

So every day the postman had
something the dogs liked to eat.

That was fun for the dogs.

It was fun for the postman, too.

The dogs thought the best time
of the day was when the postman came.

Every day they looked for him.

Our Friends

Dick and Nancy had two friends
that they liked very much.
The friends were Bob and Susan.
Bob and Susan lived down the street.

Every day the two boys
and the two girls played.
"Bob and Susan are our friends,"
said Dick and Nancy.
"They are our best friends."

One day the four friends
did not run and play.
They sat down to talk.
They were not happy.

"I don't like it," said Dick.
"I don't like it," said Bob.
"No one likes it," said Nancy.

The four friends talked on.

"We cannot help it," said Susan.
"No, we cannot help it," said Bob.
"Father has to take the best work he can get."

"Yes," said Nancy.
"And he has to take you and your mother and the baby with him."

"We will all have to go," said Susan.
"We have to go where Father has work.
It is far away.
We may never see you again."

No one talked for a long time.

Then Bob said,
"We may never see you again,
but we can send you letters and cards."
"Oh, will you, Bob?" said Dick.
"Will you send us cards
from your new home?"

"Yes, I will," said Bob.
"I will send you cards
on the way, too.
I will send you many cards
and tell you everything."
"Good!" said Dick.
"You will be far away.
But we can go on being good friends."

A New Home Far Away

"Susan," said Nancy.
"How big is the town
where you are going to live?"
"Oh, it is not big!" said Susan.
"It is just a little town."

"Little towns are fun," said Dick.
"The boys and girls in little towns
have good times."
"Yes, I know they do," said Susan.
"But I wish you and Nancy
could go with us.
Then the little town would be fun."

"The little town is in the mountains," said Bob.

"It is far up in the mountains.
Father has good work there.
He will work on the trains that come up the mountains."

"Will he have much work to do?" said Dick.

"Oh, yes!" said Bob.
"Every train that comes up the big mountains must be worked on.
Father will have helpers.
They will work on the trains.
Then the trains can go on over the mountains."

"I would like that," said Dick.
"I would like to do work like that."

"I would like to see the mountains," said Nancy.

"Susan, will you send me some cards, so I can see how the mountains look?"

"Oh, yes, Nancy, I will!" said Susan.

"The cards we send will come on trains," said Bob.

"Maybe they will come on trains my father has worked on."

"Oh, yes, they will!" said Dick.

"We will think about that every time we get a card from you."

The day came
when Bob and Susan had to go.
Dick and Nancy went to the train.

"We do not want you to go,"
said Dick and Nancy.
"But we know you will like
your new home.
Send us letters and tell us
all about the good times you have."

Bob and Susan said
they would send many letters.
Then the four friends
said "Good-by."
Bob and Susan went away
to a new home in the mountains.

From Bob and Susan

Every day Dick and Nancy
looked for the postman.
"Oh, Mr. Postman!" they said.
"Did you bring us any cards?
Our friends, Bob and Susan,
are going to send us some cards.
Did you bring them?"

"Not this time," said the postman.
"I don't have any cards
for you this time.
But they will come."

It was not long until the postman did bring cards for Dick and Nancy.

"Here they are," called the postman.

"They are pretty cards, too."

"Oh, look!" said Nancy.

"I have two cards from Susan, and Dick has two from Bob.

Mother said it would not be long until our cards came.

Oh, this is fun!"

Dick and Nancy sat down
to read the cards.
"Susan and Bob had a good time
on the train," said Nancy.

"Look at this train!" said Dick.
"It is red and black and yellow.
Look at it climb up the mountain.
Choo-choo, big train!
I wish I could ride
on a big train like that."

"Look at this card, Dick," said Nancy.
"Here the train is going over a river.
See the water in the river.
The train is going fast, too."

"Look, Nancy," said Dick.
"Here is the car on the train
where Bob and Susan stayed at night.
It must be fun
to go to bed on a train."

"I like this card best of all,"
said Nancy.
"See the big trees!
And see how big the mountains are!
The mountains do not look
like the hills we see here.
Mountains are big!"

"I wish I could go to the mountains,"
said Dick.
"Summer in the mountains
would be fun."

Many cards came from Bob and Susan.
It was not long until letters came, too.
It was fun for Dick and Nancy
to read the letters.
Bob and Susan liked their new home.
Their letters told all about it.

Susan told Nancy about the little town
and the fun the boys and girls had.
Bob told Dick about the trains
and the work his father did.

"They do like their new home,
don't they, Dick?" said Nancy.
"Yes, they will be happy there,"
said Dick.

Our Big Book

Dick and Nancy had a work room
in their home.
There were so many things they
could do in the work room.
They could make things,
and they had fun doing it.

One summer Dick and Nancy thought
they could make a blue toy boat.
They did make it, and it was
a pretty boat.
When they put it into the water,
away it went.
Dick and Nancy liked to make things.
They liked their work room.

One day Dick and Nancy
were in their work room.

They were looking at the cards
that had come from Bob and Susan.

"My, they are pretty cards!"
said Nancy.

"I wish we had a way to
keep them nice.

I don't want to put them away.

Then we would not see them.

Dick, how can we keep our cards nice
and look at them, too?"

"I will have to think of a way,"
said Dick.

"I know what we can do," said Dick.
"We can make a big book
and put our cards into it."

"A big book would be a good way
to keep our cards nice," said Nancy.
"We could look in the big book
and see all our cards.
But how will we make the book?"

"I don't know," said Dick.
"We don't have anything
to make a big book.
Can you think of anything
that would make a big book?"
"No, Dick," said Nancy.
"I cannot think of a thing."

"Oh, Dick!" said Nancy.
"I have thought of something!
Mother has a book of pretty paper.
A man gave it to her
when she had the bedrooms papered.
He said he did not want the book again.
Maybe Mother would let us have it.
Would that do for our big book?"

"Oh, yes, yes!" said Dick.
"That would make a nice book
for our cards.
We will ask Mother to let us have it."
Away ran Dick and Nancy
to ask their mother for the book.

Mother gave the book of pretty paper to Dick and Nancy.

They took it to the work room.

"It is just the thing!" said Dick.

"We can put the cards on the back of the pretty paper."

"Oh, that will be nice!" said Nancy. "Dick, is there any way we can put the cards on the paper so that we can take them out of the book? We may want to read the cards again."

"I don't know," said Dick. "I wish we could."

"I know what we can do," said Dick.
"We can put a little white paper over the ends of the cards.
Then we can take the cards out when we want to read them."

"That will be good," said Nancy.
"We will go to work."
Dick and Nancy went to work.
"This is fun!" they said.

"Look, Dick," said Nancy.

"Don't you think it would be nice to put all the cards about the train together?"

"Yes, Nancy, I do," said Dick.

So they put all the cards about the train together.

"My, that looks nice!" said Nancy.

Then they put all the cards
about the mountains together.

All the cards about the little town
where Bob and Susan lived
were put together, too.

"I wish we had some funny cards
in our big book," said Dick.
"Do we have any funny cards?"
"Oh, yes, Dick!" said Nancy.
"I have some funny ones in my room.
I will run and get them."

"See, Dick," said Nancy.

"Here are the cards that came from Grandfather and Grandmother.

We have not looked at them for a long time.

They are all funny."

Dick and Nancy looked at the cards.

They laughed and laughed.

They put the funny cards together in the big book.

Dick and Nancy took the big book to their mother.

"Mother, do you like our book?" they asked.

"Oh, yes!" said Mother.

"It is fun to look at the cards.

I like the way you put the cards in your book.

It is a very, very nice book."

Dick and Nancy thought so, too.

Other Boys and Girls

Here are two stories that Dick and Nancy liked to read. The stories are about other boys and girls. Would you like to read them, too?

The names of the stories are "Where Is Christopher?" and "The Burro That Had a Name."

Where Is Christopher?

A Girl, a Boy, and a Puppy

Linda and David were a little girl and a little boy.

Linda liked to go to the zoo. David liked to go to the zoo, too.

Christopher was Linda's and David's puppy. Christopher had never been to the zoo.

Linda and David were sorry for Christopher.

"Oh, Christopher!" they said. "You have never been to the zoo. We are sorry about that. The zoo is so much fun."

"I know what we will do," said David. "We will go to the zoo this very day, and we will take Christopher with us."

"Do you think we can?" asked Linda. "I don't think they like to have dogs at the zoo."

"Oh, I think they do!" said David. "Dogs are animals. Come on, let's go to the zoo."

Mother put some things to eat in a basket. She gave the basket to Linda and David.

"Have a good time at the zoo," she said.

Mother did not know Christopher was going to the zoo. Linda and David did not tell her about that.

It was a long way to the zoo. Linda and David had to go on the streetcar.

Away they ran down the street to get on the streetcar.

Christopher was just a puppy. He could not run as fast as Linda and David. So they put Christopher in the basket.

Linda and David took the basket together and ran as fast as they could.

Right into the streetcar they went, with Christopher in the basket.

Christopher thought that was all right. He liked to ride in the basket.

At the Zoo

When they came to the zoo, Linda and David took the basket and went in.

"We will find out about Christopher," said David. "I think it is all right for a puppy to come to the zoo, but we will ask them."

"Christopher," said Linda, "you stay right in the basket until we find out. Don't so much as put your nose out of the basket."

Just then Linda and David saw a man with a big brown bear.

The big brown bear was doing tricks for all the boys and girls to see.

"Oh, that is a good trick!" said David.

"He is a funny big bear," said Linda.

Linda and David laughed and laughed at the funny big bear and his tricks.

The man and the bear went on.
Then Linda looked in the basket.
Christopher was not there!

David looked in the basket. Christopher was not there!

"He was afraid of the bear," said David. "He ran away from the bear! Where is he?"

David saw Mr. Green, the zoo man. David ran to him.

"Where is my dog?" said David.

"Dog!" said Mr. Green. "Dog! We never let any dogs come into this zoo!"

"Oh, oh, oh!" said Linda. "We had our dog Christopher in this basket. Now he is not here. Oh, where is Christopher?"

Mr. Green was very angry. Linda and David could see how angry he was.

"We are sorry that we brought our dog into the zoo," said Linda. "But now he is lost. We must find him. Will you help us?"

Mr. Green liked dogs, so he could not stay angry very long. He said that he would help Linda and David look for Christopher.

"Maybe Christopher went to see the monkeys," said Linda.

She ran to the monkeys. There were little monkeys and big monkeys, but Christopher was not with them.

David ran the other way to look for Christopher.

"I know Christopher is not here," he said. "This animal looks like a big yellow cat. Christopher would never come here."

No, Christopher was not there.

"Oh, David!" called Linda. "Christopher may be over here playing with the pandas. He would like the pretty little pandas." But Christopher was not there.

They went to the elephants.

There was a nice baby elephant, but Linda and David did not stop to see the baby elephant. They were looking for Christopher. Christopher was not with the elephants.

Linda and David and Mr. Green looked and looked for Christopher. They looked until they could not look any longer. They went and sat down.

Linda cried. She could not help it. She cried and cried.

Mr. Green was very sorry for Linda and David.

"We must find Christopher," he said. "I know you want him, and I cannot have a dog in the zoo."

Just then they heard something.

"That is Christopher!" said Linda. "I know it is. Where are you, Christopher?"

"Christopher, where are you?" called David.

"Come here, Christopher!" called Mr. Green.

Then all at once, they saw Christopher.

"Help him, David!" cried Linda. "Help him get out!"

David ran to help Christopher. But just then Christopher jumped right out.

My! He was happy to see Linda and David!

Mr. Green laughed. "Oh, Christopher!" he said. "That was a good trick!"

Linda and David were so happy to see Christopher that Mr. Green could not be angry. He never said another thing about their dog coming into the zoo.

That was not all. Mr. Green did another nice thing. He went to get some good things for Linda and David to eat. He brought the good things back to them.

"You must take Christopher home now," said Mr. Green.

"We will, and thank you," said Linda and David. "Thank you, and good-by! Good-by!"

Christopher could not thank Mr. Green and tell him "Good-by" as Linda and David did. But he said it another way. He said "Good-by" and "Thank you" in the way a dog talks.

Then Linda and David and Christopher went home.

The Burro That Had a Name

Little Boy, Chuco

Chuco was a little boy who lived in a pretty house with his father and his mother. He had a dog and a cat who played in the garden.

Chuco's father and mother had many things from their garden to sell. They took the things to the town not far away. Chuco went with them.

When they went to town, Chuco's father rode a burro. Chuco's mother rode a burro, too. But Chuco did not have a burro. He rode with his father.

Chuco wanted so much to have a burro of his own. Every day he wanted more and more to have a burro.

One day he said to his father, "Oh, Father, when can I have a burro of my own?"

"I don't know, Chuco," said Father. "I think you are too little to have a burro of your own. We will ask Mother what she thinks about it."

Mother heard what Father said and came out into the garden. She and Father talked together for a long time.

A Burro of His Own

"Chuco," called Father, "come here." Chuco came running.

"Chuco," said Father, "Mother and I know you want so much to have a burro of your own. We think maybe you are big enough to have one."

"Oh, yes, Father!" said Chuco. "I am big enough to have a burro. When will you get him for me?"

"I will get him before long, Chuco," said Father. "When I go to town to sell the garden things, I will get you a burro."

Father did get a burro for Chuco. He brought the burro home and put Chuco on the burro's back.

"He is a beautiful burro," said Chuco. "I never saw a more beautiful burro. He is so beautiful, he must have a name."

Father laughed and laughed. "Burros never have names," he said.

"What do you call them, then?" asked Chuco.

"Oh, just 'burro'," said Father.

Chuco said no more, but all day he thought about a name for his burro.

Chuco thought, "My dog has a name. My cat has a name. They like to be called by their names. I think my burro would like a name, too."

Chuco thought and thought of a name for his burro. "It must be a good name," he said. "My beautiful burro must have a good name. I know! I will name him Pedro. That is a good name."

Chuco called his father and mother and told them he had named the burro Pedro.

Father and Mother laughed. "We never heard of a burro that had a name," they said. "But call him Pedro if you want to."

Chuco and Pedro

Chuco had a burro to ride to town now.

Every time they went to town to sell things from the garden, Father rode a burro, Mother rode a burro, and Chuco rode his very own burro, Pedro.

One day in town Father said, "We will tie the burros to this fence until it is time to go home."

Father tied his burro, Mother tied her burro, and Chuco tied Pedro to the fence. Then Chuco went on with Father and Mother.

Father and Mother had many things to do in town. It was not long until Chuco was very tired.

"I wish it was time to go home," he said. "I am tired. I think I will go and stay with Pedro until Father and Mother come."

He went back to the fence where he had tied Pedro. He saw Father's burro and Mother's burro tied to the fence, but where was Pedro?

"Pedro! Pedro!" cried Chuco. "Where are you, Pedro?"

He could not see Pedro anywhere. Pedro was gone!

Chuco saw a little girl.

"Have you seen my burro, Pedro?" asked Chuco.

The little girl laughed and laughed.

"Who ever heard of a burro with a name?" she said. Then she laughed some more.

"My burro has a name!" cried Chuco. "I must find my Pedro. Have you seen him?"

"I don't know," said the little girl. "I did see a burro going down that road. It may have been your burro."

Away Chuco went, running down the road.

Chuco ran and ran. He did not think about being tired now. He looked and looked, but he could not find Pedro.

Chuco saw a woman working in a garden. He called over the fence to her, "Have you seen my burro, Pedro?"

The woman laughed. "Who ever heard of a burro with a name?" she said. But she was sorry for Chuco. She told him she had seen a burro down by the river.

Down to the river went Chuco. But Pedro was not there.

The Lost Burro

Chuco did not know what to do. He sat down and cried.

A man with balloons came by. He had beautiful blue and green and yellow balloons. Chuco liked balloons, but that day he was not thinking about balloons.

Chuco asked the balloon man if he had seen a burro named Pedro. The balloon man laughed. "I don't know," he said. "Down that street is a man who sells burros. He has many burros."

Chuco jumped up and ran down the street as fast as he could go.

The balloon man was right. Chuco came to a fence. Inside the fence, there were many burros. Chuco had never before seen so many burros together.

Chuco ran up to a man by the fence.

"I am looking for my lost burro," said Chuco. "Is he in with your burros?"

The man looked angry. "Your burro is not here," he said. "These are all my burros. I will sell you one if you want it. All of these are my burros."

"I know my burro is here!" said Chuco. "I see him! Let me have him."

"You cannot tell one burro from another," said the man. "One burro looks just like another burro. These are my burros. Your burro is not here."

Chuco saw that the man was right. One burro did look like another. What was Chuco to do?

Chuco thought for a long time. Then all at once he knew what to do. He went up to the fence and called, "Pedro! Pedro! Come here, Pedro!"

One burro looked up. Then that burro came running from all the other burros to the fence. He put his nose over the fence. The man could see that this one burro knew Chuco.

"This is my burro!" said Chuco. "He knew his name. All other burros are just called 'burro,' but my burro is named Pedro. He knew his name when I called him."

The man was not angry now. "You are right," he said. "That burro knew his name. He must be your burro. But I never before heard of a burro that had a name!"

Chuco took Pedro home. Pedro never ran away again. And no one ever laughed at Chuco again when they heard him call his burro "Pedro!"

To be read to children

Indian Boy's Song

In my Mother's house
All day
I play and work;
All night
I sleep.

The walls come close around me
In a good way.
I can see them;
I can feel them;
I live with them.

This house is good to me,
It keeps me;
I like it,
My Mother's house.

Billy and Blaze

Here are two stories about Billy and his horse, Blaze. Would you like to read them?

One of the stories is called "Good Pony, Blaze!" The other story is called "Blaze and the Forest Fire."

Good Pony, Blaze!

Billy Wanted a Pony

Billy was a little boy who liked horses. He liked big horses and little horses. He liked black horses and white horses. He liked all the horses he saw.

Whenever he could, he had a ride on some farmer's horse. Up and down the farm roads they would go.

Billy would play that the farmer's horse was a beautiful pony. But he knew that it was just a farm horse. "Oh, I wish you were a beautiful pony!" he said.

One morning Billy's father said to him, "I have a surprise for you. Come outdoors and see the surprise."

Billy ran outdoors. There he saw a beautiful pony with four white feet and a white nose.

"Do you like him, Billy?" said Father.

"He is a beautiful pony," said Billy. "I wish I had a pony like that."

Father laughed. "This pony is yours," he said.

"My pony!" cried Billy. "Is this my pony?"

"Yes, Billy," said Father. "He is yours."

"Thank you, Father, thank you!" said Billy. "This is the best surprise I ever, ever had!"

Billy went up to the pony.

"Look, Billy," said Father. "See the pony turn his head to look at you. He likes you."

Again the pony turned his head to look at Billy. At once the pony and the boy were friends.

"Father," said Billy, "he is just the pony I have wanted so long. I think he likes me."

"Yes," said Father. "He likes you. You will be good friends."

Now Billy had a pony of his own. He had never, never been so happy before.

Work That Was Fun

Before the morning was over, Billy thought of many things to do for his pony.

"You must have a good place to stay," said Billy.

Billy went to work, and soon he had a nice place for the pony to stay.

Billy brought the pony in, and the pony liked his new home.

"Now then," said Billy, "you must have something to eat. Here is something for you, Pony."

How the pony did eat! Then he turned and came up to Billy. He put out his head to Billy. Soon he let Billy pet him.

"What a fine head you have!" said Billy. "And you have a white blaze on your nose. All morning I have been thinking about a name for you. I will call you Blaze. That is a fine name for a beautiful horse like you."

All day Billy worked for the pony. By night, Billy and Blaze were the best of friends.

Before Billy went to bed, he went out to see Blaze again. Blaze heard him coming and called to him. It was horse talk.

"Here, Blaze," said Billy, "I have something for you. It is good to eat."

Blaze thought it was fine. He thanked Billy in the way horses can.

"Blaze," said Billy, "in the morning we will have a ride. Every day we will go for long rides. Good night, Blaze."

As soon as morning came, Billy was up. He went out to take care of Blaze.

"Now, Blaze," said Billy, "I will make you nice and clean."

Billy worked and worked. It was fun to take care of a pony that was his own. Soon he had Blaze as clean as clean could be.

Then Billy climbed on Blaze's back, and they went for a ride. Billy knew how to ride a horse, and Blaze liked to have him on his back.

Away they went. It was fun for Billy, and it was fun for Blaze. They had a happy time together.

Fun in the Forest

One of the places Billy liked to ride was in the forest. There was a little road through the forest. Billy liked to look up at the big trees.

Blaze liked to go through the forest, too, but he had to take care where he put his feet down. The road was not very good. If there were open places, Blaze would run. Billy thought that was fun.

One day when Billy and Blaze were in the forest, Billy saw an old tree in the road.

"Oh," thought Billy, "we will have to find a way to go around that tree!"

But Blaze was running fast. He ran up to the tree and jumped right over it. That was a surprise for Billy.

"Oh, Blaze," he said, "I did not know you could jump like that! I am surprised that I could stay on your back, too. It was fun! We must do it some more."

It was not long until Billy and Blaze were jumping fences. Blaze would come running up to a fence, and over they would go.

Billy was never afraid when he rode Blaze. Soon he was helping Blaze in the jumps. There was not a fence anywhere around that Blaze could not jump.

The Horse Show

One day Billy saw something on a tree by the road. He stopped Blaze to see what it was.

"Oh, Blaze!" said Billy. "There is going to be a horse show soon. They want boys and girls in the show. They want horses that can jump. You and I are going to that horse show, Blaze. There will not be a horse in the show as fine as you are."

The day for the horse show came, and Billy and Blaze were there.

"See all the fine horses, Blaze," said Billy. "We will have to do our best."

But there was no time to think about it now. There went the first boy over the jumps.

Then other boys and their horses went over the jumps. Around and around they went. First a run, then a jump. Run and jump, run and jump!

Now it was time for Billy and Blaze to jump. Away they went.

First a run, then up, up, and over they went! Again and again they did it.

A man came up to Billy and Blaze and asked them to do the jumps over again. They did it, and it was like play for Blaze.

When the show was at an end, a man came up to Billy.

"Here you are, my boy," he said. "The first prize is yours. You have the best horse in the show. You are the best rider in the show. The first prize is yours."

Billy thanked the man and took the prize. Blaze put up his head, and Billy and Blaze rode out of the show as happy as they could be.

Billy and Blaze went home. Billy's father thought it was fine that they could get the first prize in the horse show.

That night Billy went out to see Blaze. He took him some good things to eat. He told Blaze what a fine horse he was.

Billy put the prize in his bedroom. He was very happy when he looked at it.

"Good pony, Blaze!" he said.

Blaze and the Forest Fire

A Happy Summer

It was a happy summer for Billy. He and Blaze were together most of the time.

Blaze would come whenever Billy called him. Then Billy would put the saddle on Blaze, and away they would go.

Blaze liked the rides as much as Billy did. Billy talked to Blaze most of the time. Blaze liked that.

"You know what I am talking about, don't you, Blaze?" said Billy. "I think you do."

One morning Billy put the saddle on Blaze, and they started out to ride through the forest. They liked the forest best of all the places they rode. There were so many things to see in the forest.

This time they went down a little road where they had not been before. Billy looked at the trees at the side of the road. They were not pretty and green. They were very brown.

"It has been a very long summer," thought Billy. "These trees have not had any water for a long time."

Billy looked up and down the sides of the road. Everywhere the trees were very brown.

Billy and Blaze came to an open place in the forest. Billy saw there had been a fire there the night before. Billy climbed down from Blaze's back to look.

"Some one stayed overnight here in the forest," said Billy. "I am glad they put out their fire before they went away. Everyone must take care of their fires in the forest in the summer time. These trees are very, very brown, and there is no water anywhere."

Billy climbed back on Blaze, and they started on through the forest.

Fire! Fire!

Billy and Blaze had gone a long way through the forest, when all at once Blaze stopped. He would not go on.

Billy did not know what to think of this. Blaze always did what Billy said, but not this time. Blaze put his four feet down on the road, and there they stayed. Billy told him to go on, but he would not go.

"My! My!" said Billy. "You always do what I want you to do, Blaze. Come on, I want to go!" But Blaze would not go.

Then Billy looked away down the road, and he saw it.

"Fire! Fire!" cried Billy. "Some one did not put out his fire. The forest has started to burn!"

"Oh, Blaze!" said Billy. "What will we do? We cannot put out the fire. Soon it will be a big fire and burn right through the forest. Then it will burn the fences and the farmhouses. We are the ones who know that a forest fire has started. We must do something."

It did not take Billy long to think what he must do. The forest fire had to be stopped. It took the farmers to do that. He must ride back and tell them the fire had started. Then many of the farmers would come and put out the fire before all the forest was burned.

"No one but you can do it, Blaze!" cried Billy. "Can you run fast enough for us to get help in time? I know you can. Come on, Blaze!"

Billy turned Blaze around, and down the road they went.

Then Billy looked back. The fire was coming very fast. Big trees had started to burn. The fire looked as if it were coming right at Billy and Blaze.

"We can never do it if we stay on the road, Blaze," said Billy. "We can make time by going right through the forest. It is not far to a farm over there, but it is a long way by the road. We can do it, Blaze, but you will have a good many jumps to make."

Billy took Blaze through the trees, and they went as fast as they could.

All at once, they came to a big wall. Blaze had never jumped so far before, but over the wall he went.

It was all Billy could do to stay on Blaze's back as they went over the wall. But stay on he did.

"Good pony, Blaze!" said Billy. "Hurry now, Blaze, hurry!"

Blaze knew they had to hurry. Billy had never seen his feet go so fast as they did now.

Hurry! Hurry!

On and on went Billy and Blaze. It was not long until the pony and the boy were tired, very tired. But they did not stop.

"It is not far to the first farmhouse now," said Billy. "I can see it through the trees."

On they went.

"Look out, Blaze!" cried Billy. "We are coming to a little river!"

Blaze was going so fast he could not stop. There was very little water in the river now, but it would take a big jump to get over.

"Oh, oh, oh!" cried Billy. "Can you make it, Blaze?"

Over the little river went Blaze. But on the other side, the horse started to go down. It looked as if Billy would go down with him.

Blaze was very tired, but soon he was on his feet again. Billy stayed on Blaze's back. "Good boy, Blaze!" cried Billy.

They lost no time. They were on their way again at once.

"Hurry! Hurry!" said Billy. "We will soon be there."

Up to the farmhouse ran Blaze with Billy on his back. The farmer ran out to see the boy and the horse.

Billy told the farmer about the forest fire. "Hurry! Hurry!" cried Billy.

In no time at all, the farmer called other farmers. They jumped into their cars, and into the forest they went.

They had to work and work and work, but they did stop the fire.

Soon a very tired horse and a very tired boy went home. The fire was out, and they could go home and go to bed. Billy was so tired, he could not talk any more.

Some days went by. By that time Billy and Blaze were no longer tired. Then they were glad, so glad, they had stopped the forest fire.

That is not the end of the story.

One day all the farmers came to Billy's house. They told Billy's father how Billy and Blaze had stopped the forest fire.

"We have a surprise for Billy and Blaze," said the farmers.

Then they gave Billy the surprise. It was a beautiful new saddle!

My! Billy was glad. "I have always wanted a beautiful saddle for Blaze," he said.

"A fine saddle for a fine horse and a fine boy!" said the farmers.

To be read to children

Young Horse Running

The young horse felt a wild wind blowing.
Wind had a voice. It said, "Be going!"

Leaves were leaping in the air.
He had to race them everywhere.

He had to find the green new clover.
There was a fence for leaping over.

Then by his pasture, on its track,
He saw the big train racing back.

He raced the train; the train was slowing
Around the bend, but he kept going.

All the wild leaves dropped to ground.
Then the horse heard a faster sound.

The small horse saw his anxious mother,
Running to him like no other.

It was long for him to roam.
He raced her, and he beat her home.

Tammie and Smoky

Do you like dogs? Do you like to read stories about them?

Here are two dog stories for you to read. One of the stories is called "There Was Tammie!" The other story is called "Smoky and the Red Fire Engine."

There Was Tammie!

Surprise Picnic

"Who is ready to go on a picnic?" called Mother, one fine morning.

"I am," said Nancy.

"I am," said Bob.

"I am," said little David.

Nancy and Bob and little David came running.

"We are always ready for a picnic, Mother," said Nancy.

"A surprise picnic!" said Bob.

"Surprise picnic!" said little David.

"Mother," said little David, "my toy bear is ready for the picnic. May I take him?"

"Yes, I think so," said Mother. "But there is not much room in our little car. You get in front and ride with me, David."

Little David climbed into the front of the car.

"Bob and Nancy," said Mother, "you must ride in the back of the car and take care of the cake."

"We will do that," said Bob.

"What a fine big cake!" said Nancy. "This is a surprise. Did you make it for the picnic, Mother?"

Mother just laughed, but little David said, "Picnic cake!"

"Bob and Nancy," said Mother, "you don't have much room back there, do you? Bob, you get on one side of the cake. Nancy, you get on the other side. I would put the cake in front, but we have the picnic basket up here."

"We are all right, Mother," said Bob.

"The cake is all right, too," said Nancy.

"Now," said Mother, "I think we are ready to go. Do we have everything? Cake, basket, water, my book to read, Bob, Nancy, David . . . . ."

"And Tammie!" cried out Bob and Nancy and little David all together.

Just then from the back of the house, Tammie came running.

"Bow-wow! Bow-wow!" said Tammie.

"Mother," said Bob, "Tammie is ready for the picnic."

"Oh, my!" cried Mother. "There is not room enough for Tammie. Where would we put him? We will have to let him stay at home this time. Yes, Tammie, you will have to stay at home and be a good little dog."

"Bow-wow! Bow-wow!" said Tammie. But he was not happy at all.

What Was Tammie Doing?

Bob and Nancy and little David and Mother rode away to the picnic. But they were not very happy.

It was a nice day, but it would not be a nice day for Tammie. What would Tammie do all day?

That is what they were thinking. Then all at once little David's hat had to blow off his head. Off it went! Mother had to stop the car. Bob had to jump out and run back to get little David's hat.

Bob started up the street, looking for the hat. Soon he saw it. That was not all he saw, for right by the hat,

THERE WAS TAMMIE!

Bob took the hat. Then he said, "Go home, Tammie, go home!"

Tammie started off. First he would go a little way, then stop and look back, stop and look back, stop and look back.

Bob went to the car and put the hat on little David's head. Then he climbed in and sat down by the picnic cake. Nancy looked back and saw Tammie turn his head and look at them.

The car went on.

"I am going to stop at the store," said Mother. "I want to get some animal cookies at the store for little David."

Mother climbed out of the car and started into the store.

"We will keep some of the animal cookies for Tammie," she said.

"Oh, yes!" cried little David. "I will keep two big elephant cookies for Tammie."

Soon Mother came out of the store with the animal cookies. When she opened the door of the store, what did she see?

THERE WAS TAMMIE!

"Tammie!" said Mother. "You cannot go with us. Go home, Tammie, go home!"

Tammie started home, but he turned around and looked back again and again.

Mother went back to the car and they rode on.

Very soon Mother had to stop to get something for the car. The man came to see what Mother wanted. All at once the man laughed.

"Is this your dog?" he asked.

Mother looked out of the car, and

THERE WAS TAMMIE!

At first Mother did not know what to think.

"Yes, thank you," she said to the man at last. "That is our Tammie. But he must go home. Now, Tammie, you go home! You go home, and you stay there!"

Tammie started home, but the last time they saw him, he was looking back at them. Mother and Nancy and Bob and little David and David's toy bear rode on to the picnic.

Tammie Would Like This

As they rode on, Bob and Nancy were thinking about Tammie. They saw so many things Tammie would like to see.

They saw three ducks going down to a little river to swim. "Quack! Quack!" said the ducks.

"How Tammie would like to swim and splash with the ducks!" thought Nancy.

They saw a hen and some little chickens. "Cluck! Cluck!" said the hen. Away the little chickens ran.

"You would run faster if Tammie were here," thought Bob.

They saw two dogs by the road. They were playing together.

"Tammie likes to play with his friends, too," thought Bob and Nancy.

A car went by and said "Honk! Honk!"

This time it was Mother who thought about Tammie. She thought of how Tammie liked to ride in the car. She thought of how he always said "Bow-wow!" when a car went by and said "Honk! Honk!"

Bob and Nancy did not care much about the picnic cake now. They wanted Tammie there in the car with them.

Little David liked his animal cookies, but he wanted Tammie, too. They all wished they had let Tammie come on the picnic.

"We will soon be there," said Mother.

Just then they heard "Honk! Honk! Honk!" A car was coming back of them. Now the car was in front of them.

They looked into the car. They could see a big man in the front, and at the side of the man,

THERE WAS TAMMIE!

The big man was Mr. Hill, who lived on their street. He stopped his car, and Mother stopped her car.

"You must have lost Tammie out of your car," said Mr. Hill. "I saw him by the side of the road. I brought him to you."

Mother looked around at Bob and Nancy. Then she looked at little David. They looked back at her, but no one said a thing.

"Thank you, Mr. Hill," said Mother at last.

Then she opened the back door of the car. "Jump in, Tammie!" she said.

They said "Good-by" to Mr. Hill and rode on to the picnic. The cake had to go down at Nancy's feet, and right where the cake had been,

THERE WAS TAMMIE!

Smoky and the Red Fire Engine

The Red Fire Engine

Clang! Clang! Clang!

"If I want to see it," thought Smoky, "I will have to hurry."

Smoky ran as fast as he could. He ran out to the street to see the big red fire engine go by. This time he was there soon enough to see it coming out of the fire house.

Clang! Clang! Clang!

Smoky ran down the street, but he could not keep up with the big red engine. He wanted to see it as long as he could. But it soon went around a turn, and he could not see it any more.

Smoky went back. He did not go home, for he had no home. There was no one to care for him. There was no one to see that he had something to eat and a good bed to sleep in. He just found what he could to eat. Every night he had to look for a place to sleep.

"My!" thought Smoky. "It would be nice to have a good home!"

Smoky liked to stay where he could see the big red fire engine. He liked the big bell on the engine. He was happy when he heard the bell go "Clang! Clang! Clang!"

Smoky was happy when he could run out to the street in time to see the engine come out of the fire house. It was fun to run down the street and try to keep up with the big red engine.

"I wish I could run as fast as the big red engine," thought Smoky. He would try to do it, but he always found out he could not.

One day Smoky was out looking for something to eat. When he went by the fire house, he saw an open door. It was not open very far, but he could look in.

He put his head inside the door to see the big red engine. There it was, ready to go to a fire. But not a fireman was to be seen.

"My!" said Smoky. "See how clean it is!" By this time, most of Smoky was through the door. Then before he knew it, he was going right up to the fire engine.

The Top of the Engine

Smoky could not see very much of the fire engine. So he jumped up on it to see more.

"My!" said Smoky. "This is fun! I will just climb up where I can see all of it."

Before he knew how he did it, Smoky was up on the big engine. There was the big bell that went "Clang! Clang! Clang!" There were the red lights that went around and around.

There were so many things to see. He jumped to one place, then another. At last he climbed to the top of the engine.

Then Smoky found a nice place to sleep. Yes, before he knew it, he had gone to sleep, right on top of the fire engine. In his sleep, Smoky thought he was a very big dog. He thought he could run as fast as the fire engine.

Buzz! Buzz! Buzz!

Smoky heard something that said "Buzz!"

"What is that buzzing?" he thought.

Then down came the men. They were the firemen, and they were ready for a fire. They climbed on the engine. The engine started. The doors opened.

"Clang! Clang! Clang!" went the bell. They were out of the fire house before Smoky could do a thing.

Smoky was not sleeping now. He was not thinking he was a big dog running as fast as the fire engine. He knew he was just a little dog and that he was on top of the big red fire engine.

"Oh! Oh!" thought Smoky. "I am on the engine, and we are going to a fire. I cannot get off now."

Down the street they went. "Clang! Clang! Clang!" went the bell. Around and around and around went the red lights.

My, how fast they went! Smoky had never gone as fast as this. He put his head up to see things go by.

"Bow-wow! Bow-wow!" said Smoky.

One of the firemen saw Smoky. "Look!" he cried. "How did that dog get on this engine?" But they could not stop, so Smoky rode on.

Up one street and down another they went. Then they came to the fire. A big blaze was coming from the top of the house.

There was work for the firemen to do. They had to put out that fire. They ran here and there. Now they had water on the blaze. Some of them went up on the house, and some went into the house.

Smoky jumped down from the fire engine. "I must not get in the way," he said.

Then Smoky saw something blow from the house. This thing had fire on it. It could burn a fireman. Smoky jumped and took the thing away.

"Good dog!" said the fireman. "You are a good fireman!"

On the street in front of the house, Smoky saw a little girl who cried and cried. She had lost her doll. "I want my doll!" she cried. "My doll is in the house. I can see it in there. Someone get my little doll before it burns up!"

But the firemen had too much to do. They could not stop to get a little girl's doll.

A Home for Smoky

More burning things were coming down on the firemen. They looked around for Smoky. They could not see him anywhere.

"Where is that dog?" cried one of the firemen. "He could help us."

"Oh, he must have gone away!" cried another fireman. "Most dogs don't like fire. He was afraid and ran home."

Where was Smoky?

Just then the little girl cried out. "Look! Look!" she cried. And everyone looked.

Smoky had not run away at all. There he was, coming out of the house. He was as black as he could be, but he had the little girl's doll!

"Look at that dog!" cried everyone.

"There is a fireman for you!" cried one of the firemen.

The little girl was glad to get her doll. She sat down in the street and cried and laughed. She told Smoky what a fine dog he was.

Now most of the fire was out. A big fireman came over to Smoky and said, "You are a good dog. I think you will have to come and live with us at the fire house. We are always looking for a good fireman."

"Yes! Yes!" cried all the firemen. "Come and be our dog. You are a fireman now."

That was the way Smoky came to have a home. Now he has a good bed and all he wants to eat. He has a fireman's hat, too. At last he has found a way to go as fast as the big red fire engine. He rides on it.

Today We Ride

Do you like rides? What rides do you like best?

Here are stories of three rides. Read the stories and find the ride you like best.

The names of the stories are "Bobby Rides a Bus," "Louise and the Subway," and "Now We Fly."

Bobby Rides a Bus

Today Is the Day

"Get up, Bobby, get up!" called Mrs. Bruce. "Today is the day you go to see Grandfather. It will soon be time for your bus. Hurry, Bobby!"

Bobby jumped out of bed and started to get ready.

Bobby was just four, but he was big for four. He knew how to put his things on. He put on his nicest things. He was going to see Grandfather today, and he wanted to look his best.

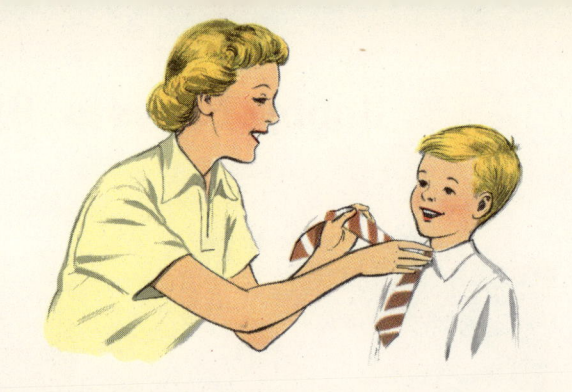

Bobby would have a long ride to Grandfather's. It would take all day on the bus.

"I wish I could go with you, Bobby," said his mother. "But I just cannot go this time. Will you be all right, Bobby?"

"Oh, yes, Mother!" said Bobby. "I can take care of myself. You know I can take care of myself, don't you, Mother?"

"Yes, Bobby, I think you can," said Mrs. Bruce. But she did wish she could go with him.

"I will have fun when I get to Grandfather's," said Bobby.

"Yes, Bobby," said Mrs. Bruce. "You will have a good time at Grandfather's farm."

Mrs. Bruce had talked to the bus driver before today. He had said that he would look out for Bobby.

"Let him go on the bus," said the driver. "Many times little boys ride on my bus. He will be all right."

Mrs. Bruce thanked him. When she went home, she thought of something. "I will make a card and put it on Bobby," she said.

She had the card ready today.

"Bobby," she said, "I will tell you what is on the card."

This is Bobby Bruce. He lives at 2 Hill Street, White River. He is going to see his grandfather, David Bruce, at his farm in Watertown.

"Oh, Mother!" said Bobby. "Must I have that card? I can look out for myself."

"Please, Bobby," said Mrs. Bruce. "Please let me put it on."

"All right, Mother," said Bobby.

Then Bobby's mother said, "Here is some money for you. You may take some of the money to get something to eat when the bus stops. Now we must go."

The Red and Yellow Bus

Bobby and his mother went to the bus. It was a big red and yellow bus.

"Look at the big bus!" said Bobby. "This is going to be fun!"

"Good-by, Bobby," said his mother. "Please do everything the driver tells you to do. Grandfather will be at the bus stop when you get to Watertown. Be a good boy."

Bobby climbed into the bus.

"Hello, Bobby," said the driver. "I was looking for you. You will have a nice ride today. Find a place you like to sit."

Bobby found a place to sit where he could look out the window.

Just then the driver came back to Bobby. He had another boy with him.

"Bobby Bruce, this is Dick White," said the driver. "Dick has had many rides on my bus. I thought you boys would like to sit together."

Bobby and Dick sat down. The bus started.

"How old are you, Bobby?" asked Dick.

"I am four," said Bobby. "But I am big enough to ride on the bus by myself. I am going to my grandfather's. He has a big, big farm. When do we stop to eat?"

"Not for a long time," said Dick. "Don't you want to look out the window and see what there is to see?"

"I see a horse and wagon," said Bobby. "I see some cows, too."

"Look over there, Bobby," said Dick. "Do you see the pigs?"

But the bus was going too fast for Bobby to see the pigs. He did see a house with many chickens in it. He saw a man with a big basket of eggs. "I like to eat eggs," said Bobby.

On and on went the bus. They rode for a long time. They went through little towns and by big farms, but the bus did not stop.

They came to the mountains. The road turned this way and that way. Up and up climbed the bus. There were no farms to see now. Big trees were everywhere.

The bus did not go fast now. The driver had to work to turn the bus when the road turned. Bobby looked at the driver in the front of the bus. All at once, Bobby was afraid.

"Don't be afraid," said Dick. "The bus climbs this road every day. It is a good road. We will soon be at the top of the mountain."

The bus did get to the top of the mountain. There, at the top of the mountain, was a little town of pretty houses. Up to the door of one of the houses went the bus. There it stopped.

"We stop here to eat," the driver called out. "You will find good dinners here."

Bobby and Dick jumped off the bus and went into the eating house.

"We are ready for dinner," they said.

The End of the Ride

"This is a nice place to eat," said Bobby.

A pretty girl in white came up to them. "What will you boys have for dinner?" she said. She gave them a card that told what they could have.

Dick helped Bobby find some good things to eat.

Just then the bus driver came to help Bobby, too. "But I see you are all right, Bobby," he said. "Dick will take good care of you."

"Oh, yes!" said Bobby. "Dick is my friend."

What a good dinner they had there on top of the mountain!

Bobby took out some of his money and gave it to the pretty girl in white.

"Good-by, Bobby Bruce," she said. "Come back again some time."

"How did you know my name?" asked Bobby.

"I saw it there on your card," said the girl.

"Oh, yes!" said Bobby. "My mother put that card there so I would not get lost."

"I will not let you get lost, Bobby," said Dick.

Then back to the bus they went. The bus started down the mountainside.

Before long, they saw farms again.

"These farms are as big as my grandfather's farm," said Bobby.

"We will be at your grandfather's very soon," said Dick.

Just then the boys saw a car on the road by the bus. It was an old car but a good one. It was going fast enough to keep up with the bus.

"There's my grandfather!" cried Bobby. "Do you see him in that car? That is Grandfather!"

"Hello, Grandfather!" Bobby called through the window. The man in the car saw him and called back.

Just then the bus stopped.

"Watertown!" the driver called out. As the driver opened the bus door, Bobby's grandfather came up.

"Hello, Bobby," said Grandfather. "Did you have a good ride on the bus?"

"Oh, yes, Grandfather!" said Bobby. "I had a very good ride. And I have a new friend. Grandfather, this is Dick White."

"Hello, Dick," said Grandfather. "It is nice that you and Bobby are friends. You must come to see us at the farm some day."

Dick said that he would come.

Then it was time for the bus to go on, so Dick had to tell Bobby "Good-by." Grandfather thanked Dick for being so nice to Bobby.

Dick said that he would send Bobby a letter soon. Bobby liked that.

Dick climbed back into the bus. The bus was ready to go.

Bobby jumped into Grandfather's car, and they started to the farm. As the car went by the bus, Bobby saw Dick looking out the window. "Good-by, Dick!" called Bobby.

Louise and the Subway

A Ride for Louise

The day started just right.

Louise jumped out of bed and looked out the window. It was a beautiful morning.

"I am so glad!" she said. "It will be a fine day! Today is the day I am going downtown. Today is the day I am going to ride on the subway all by myself."

Louise was very happy.

Grandmother had talked Mother into it.

"Louise is a big girl now," Grandmother said. "Let her come on the subway. I will meet her. I want to get a new coat and hat for her. I want to take her to a big store. I want her to find a coat and hat that she likes."

"All right," said Mother. "She may go if you will meet her."

"I will be right there when her subway train comes in," said Grandmother.

Louise had thought and thought about the new coat and hat. Would they be blue? Would they be yellow? Would they be red? She would get them today.

"Grandmother said I could have the coat and hat I like best," said Louise. "And Mother is going to let me go on the subway by myself! I must hurry."

Louise started to get ready.

"Oh, Louise!" said Mother. "You must eat first. Grandmother cannot meet you now. You must go at just the right time."

At last Mother said it was time to go. She went with Louise to the subway train.

Down the street went Mother and Louise. Then down under the street they went.

"I am not afraid," said Louise. "I know subway trains run under the streets. That is the way they have to go in a big city. There is not room for them on top of the streets. Oh, I like the big city, and I like the subway!"

"Here comes the train!" cried Louise. "Look at the big lights on the front of the subway train!"

"I don't know what you said, Louise," said Mother. "There is so much noise."

Louise was not afraid of the noise. She knew subway trains always make noise.

"Father told me the walls on the sides make the noise," Louise said.

The train came to a stop. Mother went to the first car. The trainman opened the door of the car. Right away Louise liked the trainman.

Mother told him where Louise was to get off.

"I will take good care of her," said the trainman.

"Good-by, Mother!" called Louise.

Then they were off.

Clang! Clang! Noise! Noise! Louise had never heard so much noise before, but she thought it was fun.

Louise did not want to sit by a window in the train. "You cannot see anything from a subway window," she thought. Outside everything looked black as night.

Louise sat down by the trainman. The trainman did not sit down, but he talked to Louise. He told her his name was Mr. Long. Louise told him her name and about the new coat she was going to get.

Before they had gone very far, Louise and Mr. Long were friends.

On the Subway Train

The subway train went on. It was going very fast, but it was a long ride downtown.

Just then a boy came into the car.

"Paper! Paper! Paper!" he called.

He went up one side of the car and down the other, but Louise did not see him sell any papers.

The boy stopped by Louise.

"You are not selling many papers, are you?" said Louise.

"No," said the boy. "It is not the right time of day. Where is your mother, anyway?"

Louise laughed. "I am going all the way downtown by myself," she said.

"You are not afraid, are you?" asked the paper boy.

"Oh, no!" said Louise. "I like to ride on the subway."

Then the paper boy said, "Would you like to see the funny paper?"

At first Louise thought she would do that. Then she thought not.

"No, thank you," she said. "I may not see my stop if I am reading the funny paper."

"All right," said the boy. "We are coming to my stop now. I must get off. Good-by."

The train stopped, and the paper boy was gone.

A man came into the car and sat down. He had a basket.

"My The basket looks like a little house," thought Louise. "I wish I knew what is in the basket."

When the train started, Louise looked at the basket again. She saw a little opening at one end. Through the opening, she saw a little head. "What can it be?" thought Louise.

The man saw her looking at the basket. "Would you like to see what I have in the basket?" he asked.

"Oh, yes, please!" said Louise.

The man took off the top of the basket.

"Oh, it is a puppy!" cried Louise.

"Would you like to pet the puppy?" the man asked. "You may if you want to."

"Oh, he likes me!" said Louise. "Look! The puppy likes me. Some day I am going to have a puppy of my own."

"I know you will," said the man. "Good-by. I must get off now."

Before Louise could find out the puppy's name, the man and the dog were gone.

Then on went the train.

It was not long until Mr. Long said to Louise, "We will soon be at your stop. Did you like your ride?"

"Oh, yes!" said Louise. "I like the subway. It has been fun."

"Do you know where to go when you get off the train?" asked Mr. Long.

"My grandmother is going to meet me," said Louise. "We are going to a big store to get me a new coat and hat. If you were in my place, Mr. Long, would you get a blue coat and hat?"

"I don't think I would," said Mr. Long. "You have a blue coat. Try them all on, and get the one that looks best on you."

"Thank you, Mr. Long," said Louise. "That is just what I will do."

The train was coming to a stop. Louise looked out the window. There were lights everywhere. "Oh, oh, oh!" thought Louise. "What if I cannot find Grandmother!"

Mr. Long opened the door. "Good-by, Louise," he said.

"Good-by, Mr. Long," said Louise as she went through the door.

Louise looked all around. Yes, yes! There was Grandmother!

"Grandmother! Grandmother!" called Louise. "Here I am, Grandmother!"

"My, I am glad to see you!" said Grandmother.

The New Coat and Hat

Louise told Grandmother all about her ride. She talked about Mr. Long and the paper boy. "And oh, Grandmother!" she said. "There was a man who had a puppy in a basket!"

"I can see that you had a fine ride in the subway," Grandmother said. "Now, Louise, before we go to the store, let us go and have something to eat."

"That will be fine," said Louise. "I have some money, Grandmother. Let me get something nice to eat for you and for me."

"Thank you, Louise," Grandmother said.

Grandmother and Louise went up to the street. Louise looked all around. She looked up the street. She looked down the street.

"All the houses look so big," said Louise, "and there are so many of them!"

"Yes," said Grandmother, "we live in a very big city. It is so big that the subway trains have to run under the streets."

Louise and Grandmother went to a nice place and had something to eat. Louise was glad she had some money of her own and could get something nice for Grandmother.

In the store, Louise saw blue coats, red coats, green coats, and yellow coats. She saw blue hats, red hats, green hats, and yellow hats.

"Get the coat and hat you like best," said Grandmother.

At last, Louise said, "I like the red ones best, Grandmother."

So Louise's new hat and new coat are red. Every time she puts them on, she is very happy. She calls them her subway hat and her subway coat.

To be read to children

Skyscrapers

Do skyscrapers ever grow tired
Of holding themselves up high?
Do they ever shiver on frosty nights
With their tops against the sky?

Do they feel lonely sometimes
Because they have grown so tall?
Do they ever wish they could lie right down
And never get up at all?

Now We Fly

Fun at the Farm

Bob and Nancy and little David were at the farm. Father and Mother were there, too.

They lived in the city, but they had a farm, too. Whenever Father could get away from his work in the city, they all went out to the farm. This time they were having a nice, long stay at the farm.

"The farm is fun in summer," said Bob. "But we are having more fun now. Oh, I like the farm!"

"I like the snow," said Nancy. "The snow is nicer here at the farm. There is more of it. Just look at the snow!"

There was snow on the house. There was snow on the trees. Everywhere they looked there was snow.

"Put your skis on," said Bob. "This is a fine day to ski."

Bob and Nancy knew how to ski. Little David knew how to ski, too.

"Oh, look at my ski!" said Nancy.

"Come in the workroom," said Bob. "I can make your ski all right again."

Into the workroom they went. In no time at all, the ski was ready.

"Oh, Bob!" said Nancy. "You can make everything!"

"No," said Bob, "I cannot make everything. But I can make airplanes. Look at this one. It is the best I ever did."

Nancy took up the model airplane. It was little, but it was just like a big airplane.

"It is beautiful!" said Nancy. "I wish you could put it in the model airplane show. It would get a prize."

"I am sorry about that," said Bob. "But the show is too far away. I cannot get it there in time. Come on, we will go out in the snow and ski."

"Out in the snow and ski!" said David.

Bob and Nancy and little David went outdoors and started to put on their skis.

Then they saw Father. He had on skis, and he was trying to get over the snow.

"I am not having much fun," said Father. "I never had skis on before. I don't think I can make them go."

"Oh, yes, you can, Father!" said Nancy. "We will show you how to ski. Little David can ski, so we know you can."

"David can ski!" said little David.

"Yes, you can, David," said Nancy. "But put on your mittens. You must have on mittens in the snow."

The Airplane

Over the snow came little David on his skis. He was having fun.

"Airplane! Airplane!" he cried. "I saw an airplane!"

"Where? Where?" cried Bob.

"Down the hill!" said David. "I saw it come down right on our farm!"

"Oh, no, David!" said Father. "An airplane would not come down here."

"Come and see!" said little David.

Little David, Nancy, and Bob went to the top of the hill as fast as they could.

"It is, Father! It is an airplane!" called Bob.

They could see the airplane down there in the snow.

Down the hill they went. Just as they came up to the airplane, the pilot climbed out.

Father came down the hill, too, but one ski went one way and the other ski went the other way. Then Father was upside down in the snow.

"Who is that?" asked the pilot when he saw Father.

"That is Father," said Bob. "He is not very good on skis."

"Come and help us get him out of the snow," called Nancy, who was on her way to Father.

They all helped get Father out of the snow.

"Thank you!" said Father. "Thank you very much. I don't know much about skis."

"Upside down!" said little David.

They all laughed, and Father laughed the most.

"Now, maybe we can help you," said Father to the pilot.

"I ran out of gas and had to come down before I could get to Rivertown," said the pilot.

"We can help you. I will go to the house and call the gas man. He will bring you some gas."

Father went up the hill, but not on skis this time.

Bob and Nancy and little David went up to the airplane and looked at it.

"It is a beautiful airplane," said Nancy. "It looks like a ship in the snow."

The pilot laughed and said, "We pilots sometimes call our airplanes ships."

"Take off your skis and climb into the airplane," said the pilot.

Bob and Nancy and little David climbed into the airplane.

Bob asked the pilot many things about the airplane. The pilot was surprised at the things Bob knew about airplanes.

"I am going to fly an airplane when I am big," said Bob.

"Fly! Fly! Fly!" said little David. "I want to fly."

It was not long until they saw Father coming with the gas man. The three men soon had gas in the airplane.

Then the pilot called Father to one side. He and Father talked together.

Fly! Fly!

The pilot climbed back into the airplane.

"Get ready to take off!" he said.

"Are we going to fly?" cried Nancy.

"Yes," the pilot said. "Your father said it was all right."

"Oh, Father!" called Bob. "Are you going, too?"

"No," Father called back. "But I will see you before long."

The pilot started the airplane, and it was soon blowing snow all over Father. He looked like a snow man.

The pilot found a good place to take off. Soon they were going up, up, up.

They saw Father on the hill with all their skis. They looked down on their house. The farm looked little from the airplane.

"Oh!" cried little David. "This is fun! I like to fly!"

So did Bob and Nancy. They were very happy.

"Where are we going?" Bob asked the pilot.

"I was on my way to Rivertown when I ran out of gas," said the pilot. "There is a model airplane show in Rivertown. I have to go there to give the prizes. I thought you would like to see the show. Your father said it was all right for you to go."

"Oh, thank you!" said Nancy. "We do want to see the model airplanes."

Bob thought of his model airplane. He wished he could have put it in the show. But he did not tell the pilot anything about it.

"Look, Bob," said Nancy. "See the train down there by the river."

Bob looked down and thought no more about his model airplane.

"How will we get home?" asked little David.

"Your father is coming to Rivertown in the car," said the pilot. "He will take you home."

The pilot looked down. "That is Rivertown. I will tell them we are coming down."

"Oh!" said little David. "Can you talk to them down there?"

"Yes, David," said Bob. "The man down there is talking to the pilot now."

David heard the pilot and the man talking. "Come in," said the man down there.

Down, down, down they went.

The pilot helped Nancy and David and Bob out of the airplane.

"Thank you for the nice ride," said Nancy.

"Yes, thank you," said Bob. "I am going to be a pilot some day."

"Fly! Fly!" said little David. "See me fly. I can fly like an airplane."

Model Airplanes

Bob and Nancy took little David to see the model airplanes in the show.

"Airplanes! Airplanes!" said little David.

They looked at them all. Then Bob stopped to look at a little airplane.

"Look, Nancy!" he said. "It is just like my little airplane. And it has a prize! It has the first prize."

Then he saw Father and the pilot.

"Look, Father!" he cried. "Here is a model just like my little airplane. It has the prize."

"That is your model airplane," said Father. "I brought it and put it in the show."

"Did my little airplane get the prize?" asked Bob.

"Yes, it did," said the pilot. "It is the best airplane in the show."

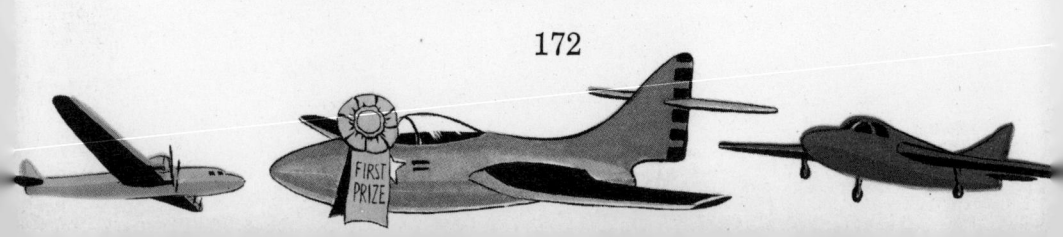

At last it was time to go home.

"It has been a fine day," said Bob. "The ride in an airplane! And now this prize!"

They thanked the pilot again for the fine ride and said "Good-by."

All the way home Bob and Father talked about airplanes.

Little David did not talk much. Soon he put his head down. He had played airplanes, he had seen airplanes, and he had been up in an airplane. He went to sleep thinking about airplanes.

Word List

The following list contains all the new words — 137 in number — that occur in *Today We Go,* basal Second Reader, Book One, of *The Macmillan Readers.* The 235 words introduced in previous books of the series, with the exception of five proper names, are repeated, making the total vocabulary of this book 367 words. Regularly inflected variants of known words formed by adding *s, 's, ed, ing, er,* and *est,* and compounds whose parts have been previously introduced, are not counted as new words.

1.
2.
3.
4.
5.
6.
7. Dick
   Nancy
8. postman
9. street
10.
11. card
12.
13.
14. end
15.
16. Bob
   Susan
17. talk
18. work
   again
19. send
20. town
21. mountains
22.
23.
24. bring
   any
25. until
26.
27.
28. their
   told
29. room
30. keep
   nice
31.
32. paper
   ask
33.
34.
35. together
36.
37.
38.
39.
40. stories
41. Christopher
   Linda
   David
42. been
   sorry
43.
44. basket
45. as
   right
46.
47. tricks
48. green
49. angry
   brought
50.
51.
52. cried
53.
54. another
55.
56. burro
   Chuco
57. sell
   rode
58. more
   own
59. enough
60. beautiful
   call
61. Pedro
   if
62. tie
   fence
63. tired
   gone
64. seen
   ever
65.
66. balloons
67. these
68. knew

174

69.
70.
71. Billy
    Blaze
72.
73. pony
74. morning
    surprise
75. turn
    head
76. place
    soon
77. fine
78.
79. care
    clean
80. forest
    through
81. an
    around
82. show
83. first
84. prize
85.
86. fire
    most
    saddle
87. started
    side
88. glad
89. always
    burn
90.
91.

92. wall
    hurry
93.
94.
95.
96.
97.
98.
99. Tammie
    Smoky
100.
101. picnic
     ready
102. front
     cake
103.
104. bow-wow
105. hat
     off
106.
107. store
     cookies
108.
109.
110. last
111.
112. honk
113.
114.
115. engine
     clang
116. sleep
     found
117. bell
     try

118.
119. top
     lights
120. buzz
     men
121.
122.
123.
124.
125.
126.
127. today
128.
129. Bobby
     bus
130. myself
131. driver
132. please
     money
133.
134. sit
     window
135.
136.
137. dinner
138.
139.
140.
141.
142.
143. Louise
     subway
144. meet
     coat

145. under
     city
146. noise
147.
148.
149.
150.
151.
152.
153.
154.
155.
156.
157.
158. fly
     having
159. snow
     ski
160. airplane
     model
161.
162.
163. pilot
164.
165. gas
166.
167.
168.
169.
170.
171.
172.
173.

175